Journey Through™ Calculus
User's Guide

Journey Through™ Calculus

Bill Ralph
in conjunction with James Stewart

User's Guide

written by
Kerry Thompson

BROOKS/COLE PUBLISHING COMPANY

I(T)P® An International Thomson Publishing Company

Pacific Grove ▪ Albany ▪ Belmont ▪ Boston ▪ Cincinnati ▪ Johannesburg ▪ London ▪ Madrid
Melbourne ▪ Mexico City ▪ New York ▪ Scottsdale ▪ Singapore ▪ Tokyo ▪ Toronto

Publisher □ *Gary W. Ostedt*
Media Editors □ *Pat Waldo and Marlene Thom*
Market Development Editor □ *Kevin Connors*
Marketing Team □ *Caroline Croley and Debra Johnston*
Ancillary Editor □ *Carol Benedict*
Production Editor □ *Jamie Sue Brooks*

Permissions Editor □ *May Clark*
Interior Design □ *Stephanie Kuhns*, TECH·arts
Cover Design □ *Vernon Boes and Bob Western*
Manufacturing Buyer □ *Barbara Stephan*
Typesetting □ *Stephanie Kuhns*, TECH·arts
Printing and Binding □ *WebCom*

For more information, contact:

BROOKS/COLE PUBLISHING COMPANY
511 Forest Lodge Road
Pacific Grove, CA 93950
USA

International Thomson Publishing Europe
Berkshire House 168-173
High Holborn
London WC1V 7AA
England

Thomas Nelson Australia
102 Dodds Street
South Melbourne, 3205
Victoria, Australia

Nelson Canada
1120 Birchmount Road
Scarborough, Ontario
Canada M1K 5G4

International Thomson Editores
Seneca 53
Col. Polanco
México, D. F., México
C. P. 11560

International Thomson Publishing GmbH
Königswinterer Strasse 418
53227 Bonn
Germany

International Thomson Publishing Asia
60 Albert Street
#15–01 Albert Complex
Singapore 189969

International Thomson Publishing Japan
Palaceside Building, 5F
1-1-1 Hitotsubashi
Chiyoda-ku, Tokyo 100-0003
Japan

Printed in Canada

10 9 8 7 6 5 4 3 2 1

Contents

Journey Through™ Calculus
User's Guide

Introduction

Welcome to *Journey Through™ Calculus*—a new, interactive CD-ROM that helps you explore and appreciate the dynamic world of calculus. It contains stunning animations and game-like activities as well as tutorials, unlimited problems and tests, and a Maple®-supported computer algebra system that help you learn real mathematics. As you journey through this multimedia adventure, you will see the concepts of calculus unfold before your eyes as you actively develop your intuitive understanding into concrete conceptual knowledge.

This booklet is a brief guide to *Journey*. It explains how to install the program; how to navigate through *Journey's* rich terrain; and how to best take advantage of *Journey's* unique features such as the Computer Algebra System (CAS), the Problem Wizard, the Test Wizard, the animations, explorations, and links to the Stewart family of textbooks.

But *Journey* is an *interactive* learning environment that needs to be experienced. For now, here's just a sneak preview of the features to look out for on your journey.

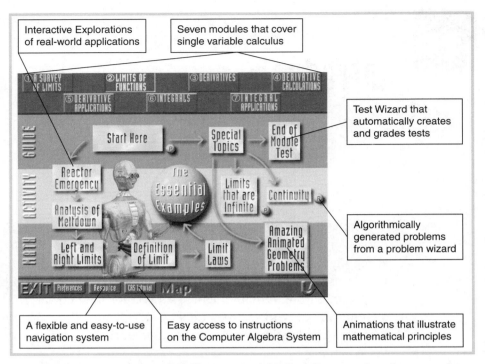

And most important, a powerful Computer Algebra System that lets you do mathematics in real time—graph functions, differentiate, integrate, and perform other calculations.

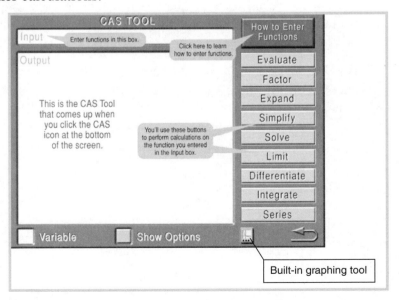

We will cover all these features in depth in the following chapters. For now, let's get the program up and running.

Getting Started

You will need a computer running Windows 95® or later, with a CD-ROM drive, at least 8 MB RAM, and 1 MB VRAM.

Before you install *Journey Through Calculus,* be sure to exit all other programs. Insert the *Journey Through Calculus* CD-ROM into the CD-ROM drive. It will automatically start the installation program; be patient, though, because it may take several seconds to start.

If the CD-ROM doesn't start automatically, do the following:

1. Click "Start" on the Windows Task Bar.

2. Click "Run."

3. Click "Browse."

4. In the dialog box that appears, open the "Look in:" drop-down menu and click your CD-ROM drive. It will probably be drive D: or E: and should be recognizable by the CD icon beside the drive letter.

5. Double-click "JTC.exe." The install program should now run.

You will see the following screen:

If you have sufficient hard disk space available (at least 500 MB) and want the best performance and most convenience, choose Option 1. This selection will guide you step by step through the installation process. Once installation is completed, you will have the entire *Journey Through Calculus* on your hard disk and will no longer need to use the CD-ROM.

On the other hand, if you do not wish to devote that much disk space to *Journey,* choose Option 2. You will then need to insert the CD-ROM in the computer every time you run the program. Also, *Journey* will run more slowly as you move between modules and probably as you move from screen to screen. However, the speed of the animations and calculations will not be affected.

If you decide not to install or run the *Journey* at this time, simply click the "Cancel" button.

That's it! You are now ready to begin your journey. Pack warm clothes, and don't forget extra batteries for your laptop.

2 Navigation

■ The Opening Menu

After a couple of introductory screens, you will see the following menu:

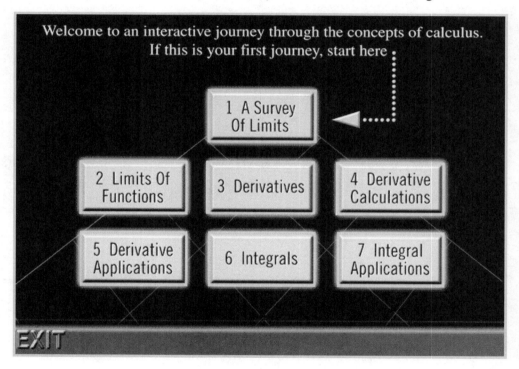

Choose any of the seven modules by clicking the appropriate button. Naturally, if you are just getting started, you will want to select Module 1, A Survey of Limits.

We recommend that you work through the modules in order, as each module builds on concepts from the previous one. You can also use this menu to review a specific module. When you feel comfortable enough with the concepts, you can even do the modules out of order.

■ Navigation Within a Module

Journey provides a flexible, easy-to-use navigation system. All modules follow the same basic scheme, so we will look at Module 1, A Survey of Limits, as our example.

When you first start a module, you will see an opening screen such as the following:

Click the forward arrow on the right. You will be presented with a menu similar to this one from Module 1:

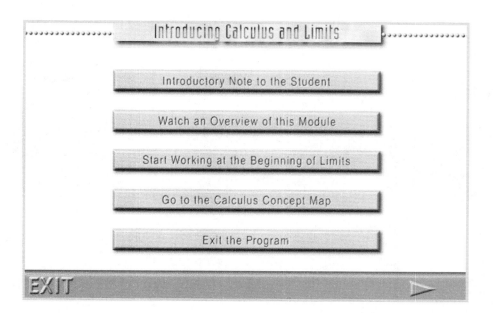

To go to *Journey's* main navigation interface, click the fourth button, "Go to the Calculus Concept Map." This option is available in the menus of all seven modules. Clicking this button brings up the following screen:

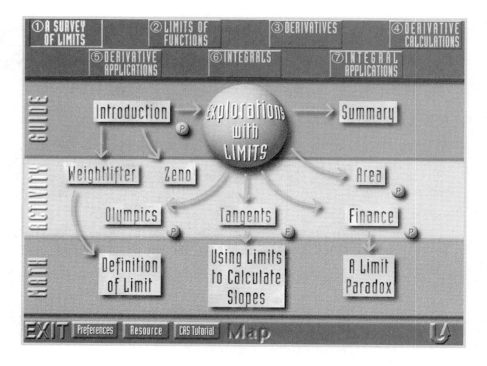

Because this is the heart of *Journey's* flexible and powerful navigation system, we will take a close look at each element of the map.

Titles Menu

The top part of this map is a menu that allows you to go to any of the seven modules. Say you were exploring Derivatives in Module 3, you could go back to Module 2 to review limits of functions simply by clicking the second button, Limits of Functions. You could also return to Module 3 after your review, and continue where you left off.

Track Menu

The center part of the map lets you decide which track to follow on your journey. There are three tracks, as shown here:

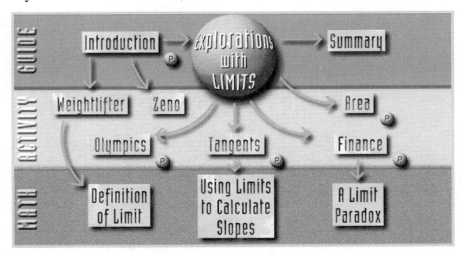

As advertised, the Guide track guides you through the concepts presented in the module, moving you along from screen to screen. The Activity track allows you to select any activity to further enhance your understanding of the module's concepts. And the Math track provides in-depth mathematical explanations of the module's concepts.

Looking at the map, you can see several arrows that show the module's flow. For example, if you click the Introduction button, *Journey* will guide you through the introduction and the Weightlifter activity, then to a Definition of a Limit on the Math track. From there, *Journey* will explore Zeno's paradox in the Activity track, then suggest that you explore another activity.

Of course, you do not have to follow the Guide track. You can click any button on the map and be taken directly to that part of the module.

One of the most important features of this three-track map is easy to miss. Look closely at the map again, and you will see the 🅿 icon in five different places. Clicking this icon causes *Journey's* Problem Wizard to create a problem for you to solve. Problems are generated algorithmically, so each time you click this button you see a different problem. We will discuss the Problem Wizard in more detail later, but for now, we urge you to use this feature to practice applying the concepts you learn.

Navigation Bar

At the bottom of the map is the navigation bar, which looks like this:

Let's start on the far right. The U-shaped arrow 🔄 takes you back to the *Journey* screen you were on before you came to the map. You will see this icon repeatedly throughout *Journey*.

The [Preferences] button brings up the following dialog box:

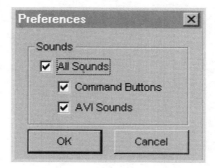

It is here that you set which sounds you wish to play. We haven't said much about the multimedia aspects of *Journey* yet, so let's take a moment to do so.

Multimedia, if you are not familiar with the term, is exactly what it sounds like: something that involves multiple media, such as graphics, sound, video, animation, photos, and text.

Journey uses several media to guide you through your calculus adventure. One of these is sound, which brings us back to the Preferences dialog box. *Journey* uses sound in two ways. One use is the "click" you hear when you click a button or the forward arrow to advance to the next screen. The other use, referred to in the Preferences dialog box as "AVI Sounds," is audio such as the narration that explains what is happening during an animation or the sound effects of a robot rumbling along a track.

You can turn these sounds on or off at will. Simply bring up the Preferences dialog box and uncheck the sounds you do not want to hear. For example, if you are working in a library or crowded lab, you might want to turn the sounds off out of courtesy to others working around you. When you work alone at home or in your dorm room, though, you will probably want to turn the sounds back on, because they are designed to enhance your learning experience.

Pay special attention to the **Resource** button. For such a small icon, this button is surprisingly important and versatile. It amounts to no less than a table of contents, right on the map. Further, it is one of the ways that *Journey* is linked with James Stewart's series of calculus textbooks. Let's look at this button further.

When you click the Resource button, you will see the following pop-up menu:

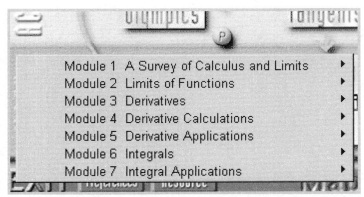

Clearly, these are immediately recognizable as *Journey's* seven modules. Unlike the opening menu or the Titles Menu at the top of the map, this pop-up menu is not just another way of accessing a particular module. It is far more powerful than that.

Notice the arrows to the right of each module title. They indicate that there are more options within that selection. Move the cursor to "Module 1 A Survey of Calculus and Limits" and you will see a second menu cascading off the module title. It will look something like the following:

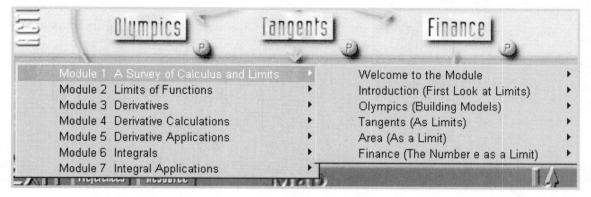

Think of these menu items as the section headings of the module. (The menus may cascade in a different direction on your monitor, depending on your screen resolution. Whichever side the new menu shows up on, it should look familiar.) Let's take another look at this menu, with the full map.

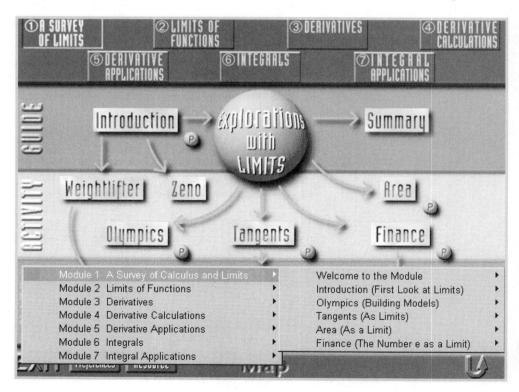

Compare the secondary menu (shown on the right here) with the map. You will find that every menu item has a matching button on the map, except for "Welcome to the Module." Again, each menu item has an arrow to the right, meaning there are more selections to come. Let's try a couple to see where they lead us.

Move the cursor to the first selection, "Welcome to the Module," to bring up one final menu.

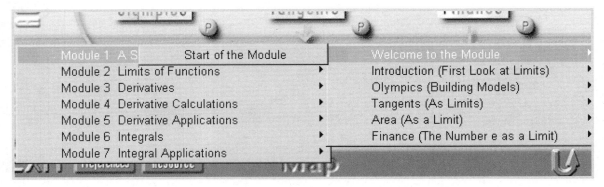

Notice that this time the choice, "Start of the Module," cascaded to the left. Again, that may vary with your screen resolution. If you place the cursor on "Start of the Module" and click the mouse, you will be taken to the opening screen of the module, as shown:

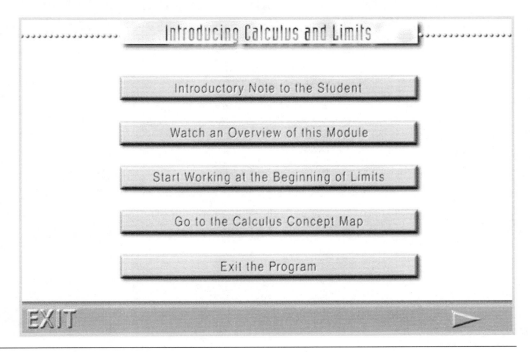

This screen should look familiar; it is the first menu you saw when you started Module 1.

You can get to virtually any point in *Journey* from the Resource menu—even places that aren't on the map. Let's take a look at your options if you choose a different selection.

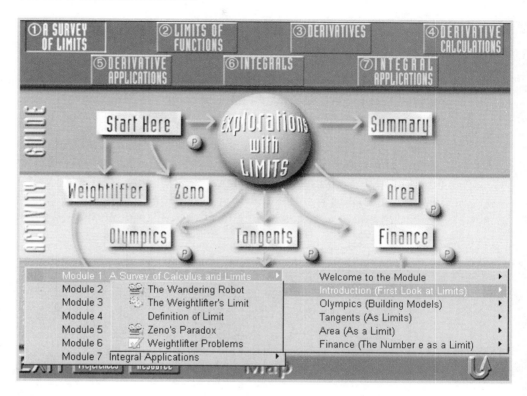

In this instance, we chose the heading "Introduction (First Look at Limits)" and got a different-looking menu. Right away you will notice that not all the menu items are shown on the map. Specifically, "The Wandering Robot" is absent. Thus, you've learned that the Resource menu is more complete than the map. It does not list every single screen in *Journey*, but the Resource menu will take you to the starting point of every major activity or concept.

The other new element in this menu is the addition of icons to the left of the headings. This menu is a good example, because it contains all three of the icons you will see in the Resource menu.

 A movie projector is the icon for animations. *Journey* contains a large number of animations that illustrate mathematical principles, so you will see this icon a lot.

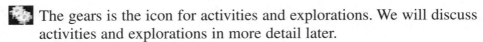 The gears is the icon for activities and explorations. We will discuss activities and explorations in more detail later.

The checkmark is the icon for a problem or a quiz. *Journey's* Problem Wizard and Test Wizard generate problems and quizzes algorithmically, giving you a different problem or test each time.

Other Navigation Icons

As you progress through your journey, you will come across other navigational icons. We will take a look at some of them now.

An icon that is every bit as powerful and important as the Resource button is the globe, . Although not shown on the module concept maps themselves, this globe icon is on nearly every screen throughout *Journey* and will bring you to the module concept map. Together with the Resource button, the globe icon forms the foundation of *Journey's* navigation system, ensuring that you have access to all parts of the program no matter where you are.

In the previous screen, notice the lock icon 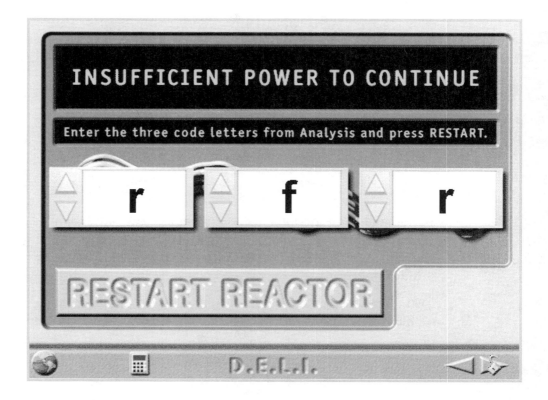 on the forward arrow. This icon indicates that you should answer the question on the screen before continuing. Assuming you have solved the problem here and entered the correct codes, you will see the open-lock icon, ⚿, as shown in the screen below, indicating that you may continue to the next screen.

INSUFFICIENT POWER TO CONTINUE

Enter the three code letters from Analysis and press RESTART.

r   f   r

RESTART REACTOR

D.E.I.I.

But what if you do not wish to do this activity? Perhaps you have already done it or are comfortable enough with the concept to move on. After all, it is your journey, and you should be able to go at your own pace, to whichever topic you wish to study.

In that case, click the locked right arrow without answering the question. You will see a screen such as the following:

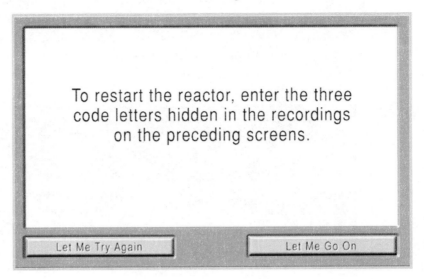

If you click "Let Me Go On," the forward arrow will be unlocked and you can proceed (but you will not see the answer). Use this option judiciously; after all, skipping too many activities would defeat the purpose of working through *Journey*.

Two other icons that you will encounter are the ▦ and the ▱, as shown on the following screen:

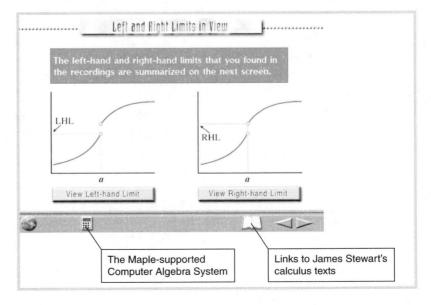

The Computer Algebra System (CAS) icon, 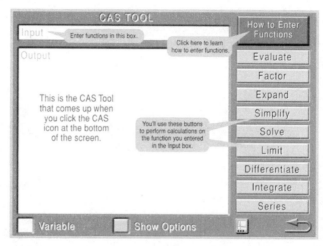, is available on many screens throughout *Journey*. This Maple-based CAS is an extremely powerful tool and a crucial part of how *Journey* helps you learn. We will discuss the computer algebra system in detail in a separate chapter. For now, though, if you want to start using the CAS immediately, you need to understand how to enter functions.

You may remember from the Introduction that the **CAS Tutorial** icon brings up the following screen:

This instruction screen does not have any active buttons, but serves as a good introduction here—the live CAS looks exactly the same, except without the instructions. To use the CAS, click the icon when it's available, and the active CAS screen will appear. From the CAS, when you click the **How to Enter Functions** button, you will see the following screen:

How to Enter Functions

To Enter	Type In
$3x$	3*x
x^2	x^2
$x^2 - 3x + 5$	x^2-3*x+5
$\dfrac{x^3 - 5x^2}{x^4 + 1}$	(x^3-5*x^2)/(x^4+1)
$\sin x$	sin(x)
e^x	exp(x)

Take a moment to study the preceding instructions. We will cover them in more detail in Chapter 4, but you should start with a basic understanding of how *Journey* expects you to enter functions.

The textbook icon, 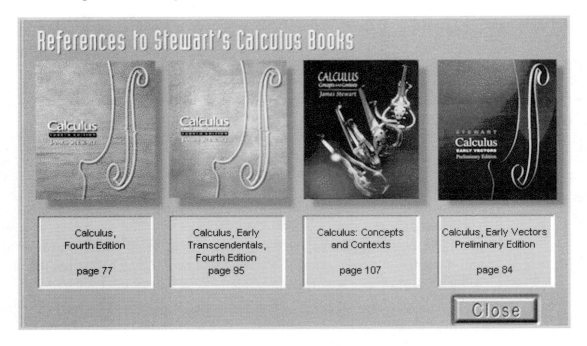, which appears only on certain screens, indicates link between *Journey* and the suite of calculus textbooks by James Stewart. Although it was conceived and written as an independent program that covers the concepts of single variable calculus, *Journey* is nevertheless closely tied to Stewart's calculus textbooks. At certain points in the program you will see this textbook icon onscreen, telling you there is a direct reference to this topic in one of Stewart's books. Click this icon to bring up the following screen:

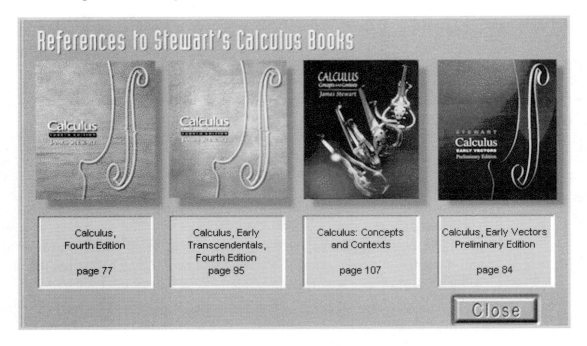

As you can see, there are specific page references to each of the four Stewart titles. If you were to look, for instance, on page 77 of *Calculus, Fourth Edition,* you would find a discussion of Left-hand and Right-hand Limits.

That does it for the Navigation section. In the following chapters, we will explore the special features *Journey Through Calculus* has to offer.

3

Explorations

The interactive explorations in *Journey* provide one of the most powerful direct-learning experiences you are likely to encounter in your study of calculus. The philosophy behind them is simple: provide an interesting, easy-to-use interface that makes learning both intuitive and fun.

Journey's explorations present calculus concepts using real-world applications. Many are introduced by an engaging animation, such as the "Analysis of a Meltdown" in Module 2. The real power, though, comes in what follows. The explorations are designed to first let you solve the problem intuitively; then the mathematical principles behind the problem are explained so you can see how to apply calculus to solve the problem faster and easier.

■ The Weightlifter's Limit

Let's take a look at a fairly simple exploration to see how *Journey* has accomplished this ambitious goal. One of the first explorations you will encounter is "The Weightlifter's Limit" in Module 1.

The following screen introduces you to the exploration:

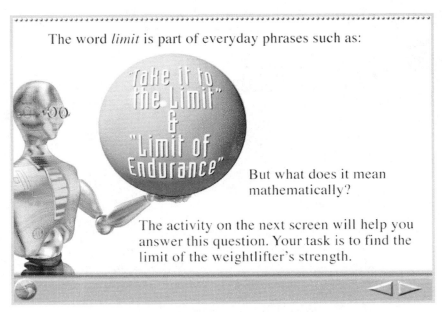

The word *limit* is part of everyday phrases such as:

"Take it to the Limit" & "Limit of Endurance"

But what does it mean mathematically?

The activity on the next screen will help you answer this question. Your task is to find the limit of the weightlifter's strength.

This screen tells you the concept you will explore (limits), and your task. Other explorations may use an animation or other type of introduction.

When you click the forward arrow, you will be taken directly to the following screen:

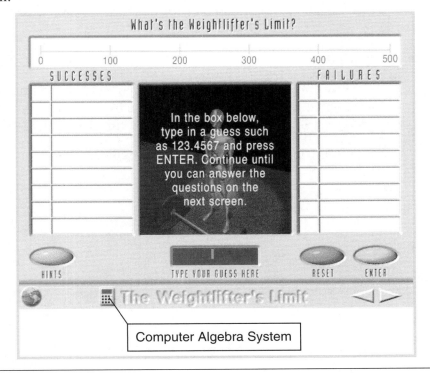

What's the Weightlifter's Limit?

| 0 | 100 | 200 | 300 | 400 | 500 |

SUCCESSES   FAILURES

In the box below, type in a guess such as 123.4567 and press ENTER. Continue until you can answer the questions on the next screen.

HINTS   TYPE YOUR GUESS HERE   RESET   ENTER

The Weightlifter's Limit

Computer Algebra System

Notice *Journey*'s Computer Algebra System (CAS) icon, . We will take an in-depth look at the CAS in Chapter 4. For now, though, there is very little math involved in this activity; as promised, this is an intuitive approach to solving the problem. Before you read further, take a moment to consider how you would approach this problem. What is the logical first guess, and how would you proceed from there? When you have come up with an approach, continue reading below to see our strategy.

A basic principle of problem solving is to look for patterns. Once you understand a problem, look for any clues in the problem itself. This exploration is asking you for a guess, but it doesn't have to be a wild guess. Take a look at the top of the screen:

There is your first clue: the weightlifter's limit is somewhere between 0 and 500. The logical first guess would be right in the middle, at 250.

Type in 250 and click Enter. The weightlifter's limit changes each time you work this exploration, so 250 may be above or below its limit. If it is above its limit, the robot will attempt to lift the weights and fail.

If your guess is below its limit, the robot will succeed.

In either case, your result will be posted in the "Failures" or "Successes" column, and you get to make another guess.

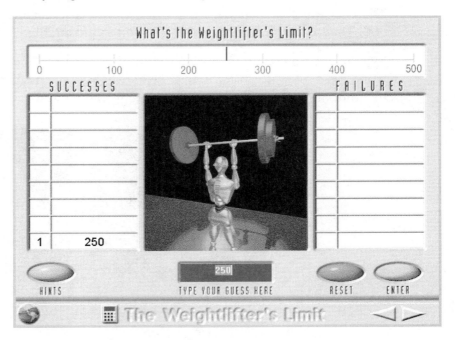

In this case, the robot succeeded, so we know that its limit is greater than 250. The next logical guess would be, again, halfway between the two numbers—now 250 and 500. As you continue slicing and dicing, you will close in on the robot's limit. You will end up with a pattern similar to the following:

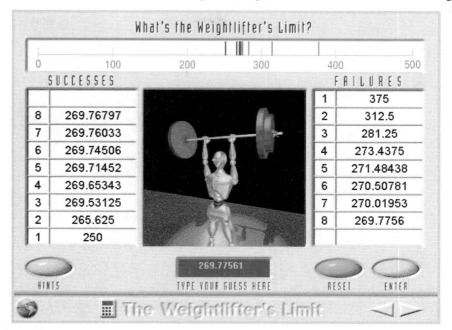

Do you know what the weightlifter's limit is? You are down to a difference of only 0.0038775 between the last success and failure. Click on the right arrow to see what *Journey* has to say about limits.

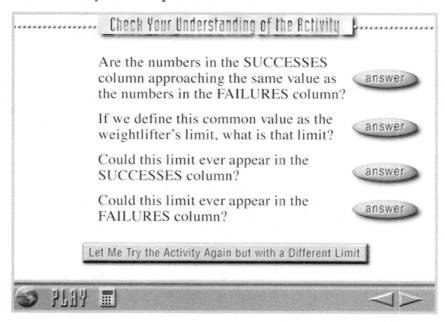

The mathematical concepts lie behind the buttons. Think about the questions posed, then click the button to see the concept. You should see the following four screens:

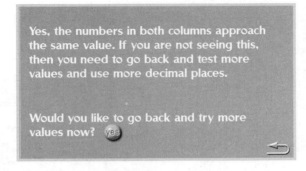

Yes, the numbers in both columns approach the same value. If you are not seeing this, then you need to go back and test more values and use more decimal places.

Would you like to go back and try more values now? yes

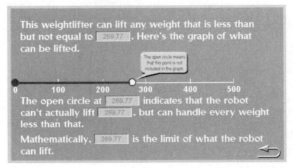

This weightlifter can lift any weight that is less than but not equal to 269.77 . Here's the graph of what can be lifted.

The open circle means that this point is not included in the graph.

0   100   200   300   400   500

The open circle at 269.77 indicates that the robot can't actually lift 269.77 , but can handle every weight less than that.

Mathematically, 269.77 is the limit of what the robot can lift.

As you can see, the robot can lift every weight less than 269.77 but not equal to it. For this reason, the weightlifter's limit of 269.77 will never appear in the SUCCESSES column.

The concept to understand is that the robot can approach 269.77 as closely as it likes but can never actually reach 269.77 .

Yes, this number can appear in the FAILURES column. If you test the number 269.77 , you will find that the robot fails.

The numbers in the FAILURES column approach and can actually reach the weightlifter's limit.

For a definition of limits, click the right arrow on the main screen. You will see the following definition:

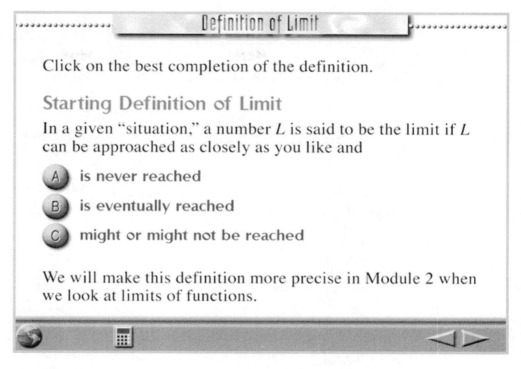

You should be able to complete the definition of limits now by choosing A, B, or C. Which do you think is the correct definition? *Journey* will confirm or correct your choice.

■ The Greedy Boss: Area as a Limit

"The Weightlifter's Limit" is a fairly simple exploration, with relatively little math involved. To really understand the power of the explorations, let's jump to Module 6, Integrals, and look at the "Greedy Boss Story," which introduces the concept of area as a limit. This exploration actually comprises three explorations in one.

Navigation

Remember from Chapter 2, Navigation, that you can reach this activity a number of ways. You can start at the beginning of the module and work through it until you reach the Greedy Boss exploration. A second choice would be to click the button on the module map:

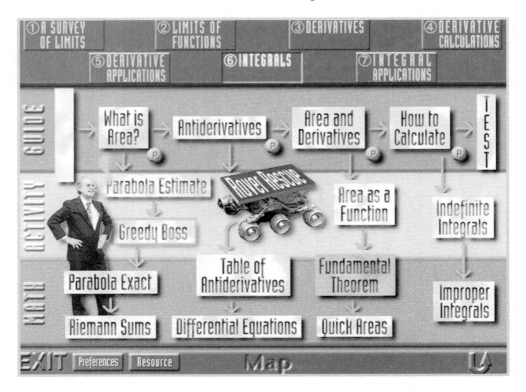

The third choice would be, of course, the Resource menu:

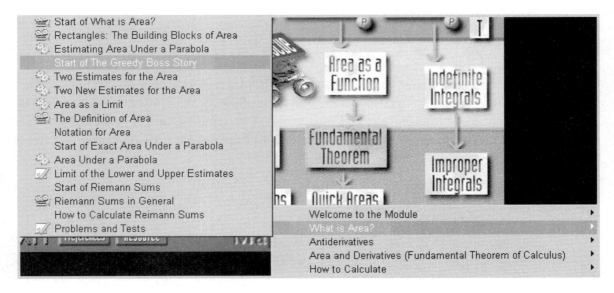

The Intuitive Approach

Whichever path you choose, you will arrive at the following opening screen, with a narrator explaining the upcoming explorations:

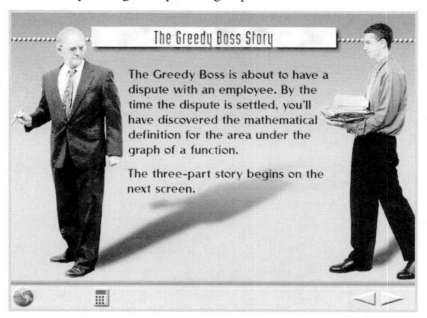

When you have heard the narrator's introduction, click on the right arrow to go to the explorations. You will get the following, which we will call the "briefcase screen":

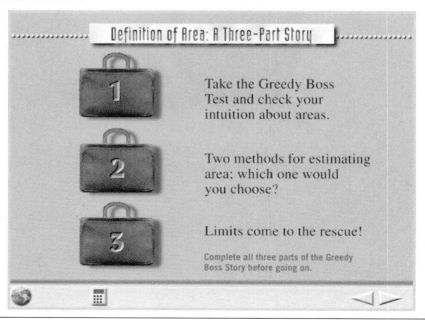

Click the first briefcase to start part 1 of this exploration.

The briefcase opens to introduce the Greedy Boss. Click it again to bring up the following introductory screen:

Click the forward arrow to move to the intuitive part of the exploration.

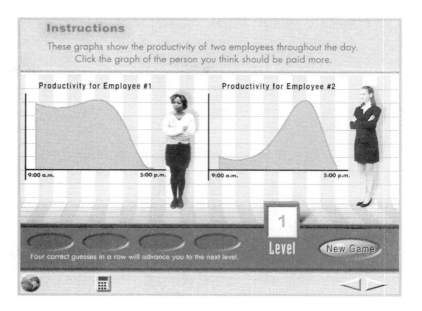

You can see at a glance that the shaded area of the graph on the left is greater than that on the right. Click the graph on the left, and one of the ovals at the bottom will turn green, indicating a correct answer. *Journey* then generates another pair of graphs, and you choose again. Each time you get a correct answer, another oval turns green. Be careful, though—if you guess wrong, all the ovals revert to gray, and you have to start over.

In the following graphic, you have gotten three correct answers in a row:

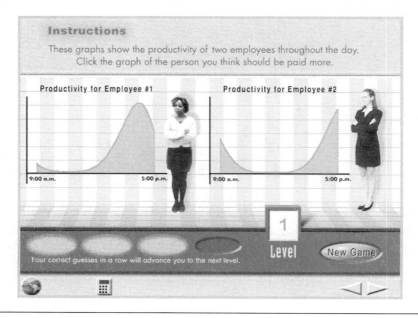

One more correct answer, and you advance to level two.

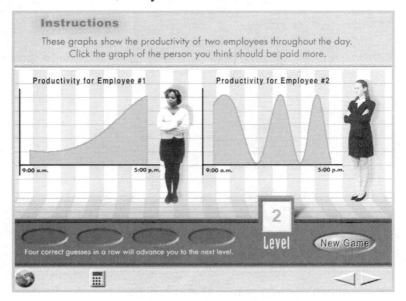

It is a little tougher to tell which graph has a larger shaded area now—the preceding graphs, from level 2, cover an area that is closer than those in level 1. The guessing gets a little tougher as you advance to each level, much as the going gets tougher the further you advance in *Tomb Raider*®. But make no mistake: even though this activity is fun and intuitive, you are learning about one of the basic concepts of calculus, area under a curve as a limit.

When you have completed all five levels,

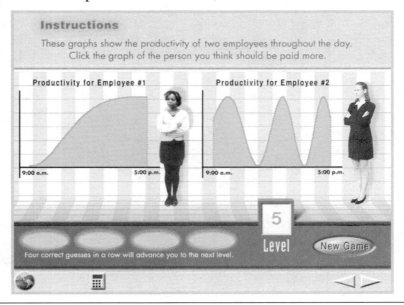

you get your reward screen:

Being a greedy boss may not be your goal in life, but it's nice to be recognized for your accomplishments—even if the congratulations has a bit of wry humor.

When you click ok, you will be given the chance to repeat the first part of the exploration. You should go through the exploration as many times as you need to become comfortable with the concept.

When you are ready to move on to part 2, click the forward arrow, and *Journey* will explain a bit about the concept you have just explored and offer a hint on what is in store for you as you continue on to parts 2 and 3.

Click the return icon ↻ to continue with the exploration. You will be taken to the briefcase screen again, where you choose the second briefcase, "Employee Fights With Greedy Boss." *Journey* introduces you to the second part of the exploration with the following screen:

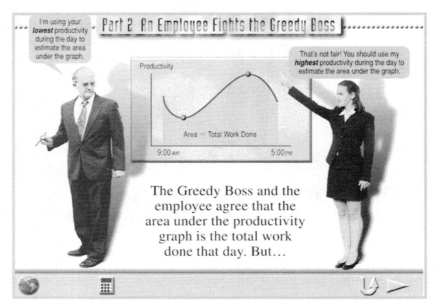

Who do you think is fair? The boss? The employee? Neither? Both? The next screen takes you another step closer to understanding the concept.

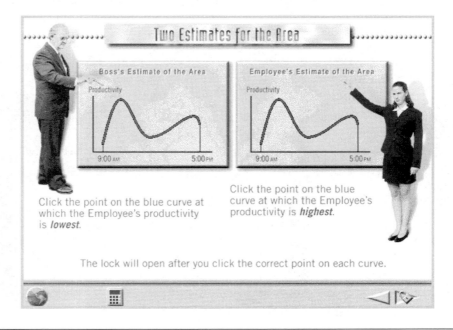

Once again, trust your instincts—you can easily spot the high and low points of the employee's productivity. By the way, notice the lock on the right arrow; this screen presents one of those crucial concepts that is so important we believe you should not simply skip over it.

When you have chosen the correct points, *Journey* leads you one more step through the exploration:

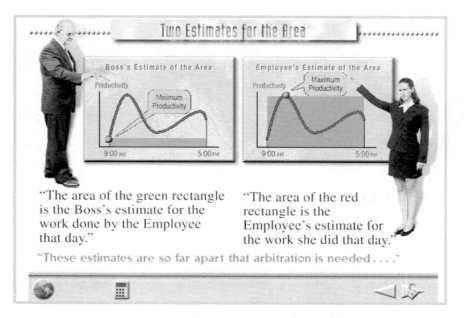

Notice that the right arrow is now unlocked; you may click it to go to the next screen.

There is quite a difference between the employee's productivity, depending on which point is chosen. If you were the arbitrator, how would you solve the difference? Think about it for a moment before turning the page to see the arbitrator's suggestion.

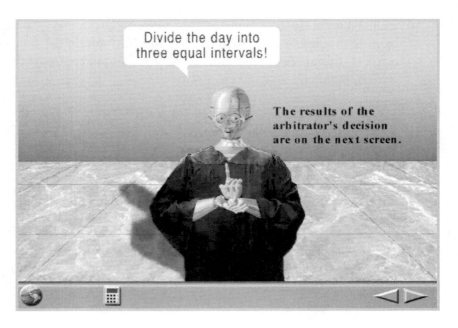

What do you think of the arbitrator's suggestion? Will it bring the boss and employee closer together or farther apart? Or will it make any difference at all? The next screen gives you the chance to participate in the new estimates:

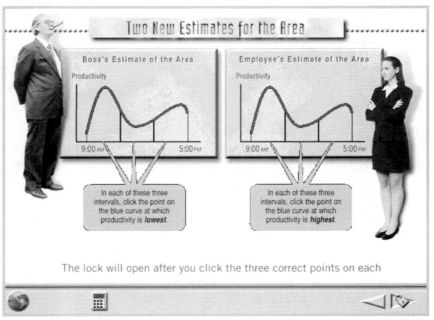

As you make the correct choice in each interval, the area beneath the point will fill in. The screen will look like this when you have correctly identified all six points:

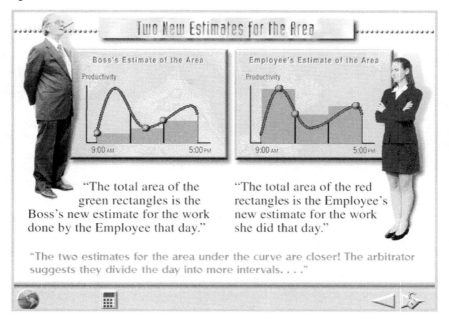

The Concept Explained

You should have a sense of where the exploration is going by now. Click the right arrow to see *Journey*'s summary of this section of the exploration, and a hint about what is to come:

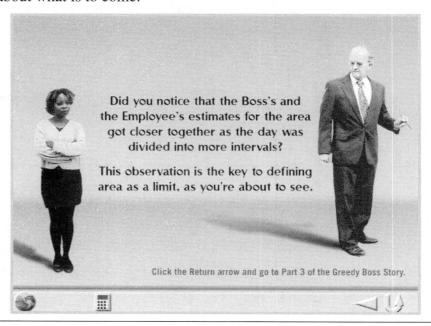

Once again, click the 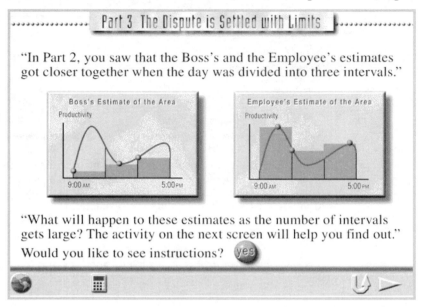 icon to go back to the briefcase screen, where you will click the third briefcase to start the third and final part of this exploration.

First, *Journey* reviews the concepts you have covered so far in this exploration. After you have read the screen, if you would like to see instructions, click the "yes" button; otherwise, click the right arrow. The next screen has several features:

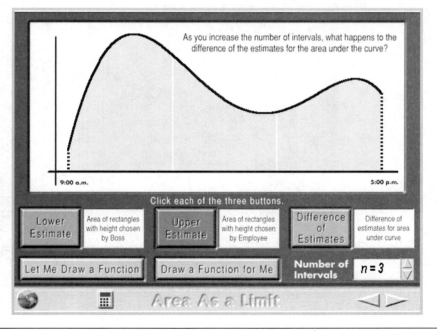

You should check each of the options on this screen. First, look at the lower estimate:

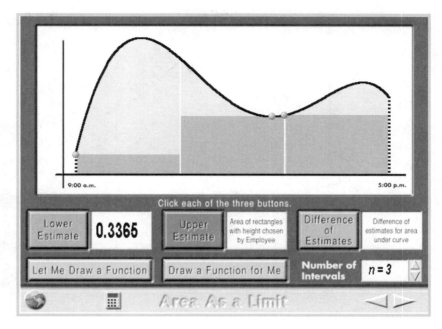

This graph should look familiar: it is the boss's choice for measuring productivity. Likewise, the graph of the upper estimate

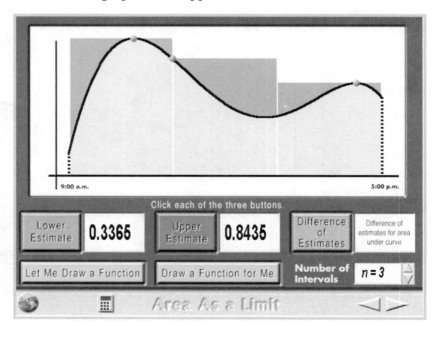

is the employee's choice for measuring productivity. Click "Difference of Estimates" to see how far apart the estimates are:

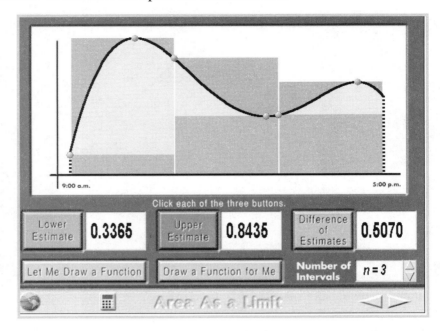

Try changing the Number of Intervals. How do you think that would change the difference between the estimates? *Journey* will show you:

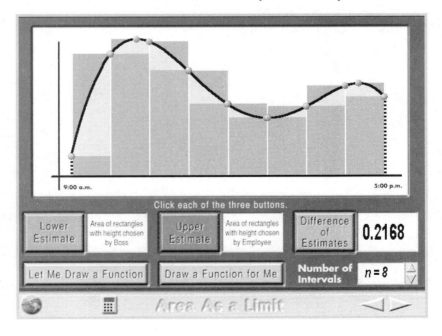

You can choose either to draw your own function or let *Journey* draw the function for you. In the following screens, you have chosen to draw your own function. First, *Journey* gives you the instructions for creating your own function:

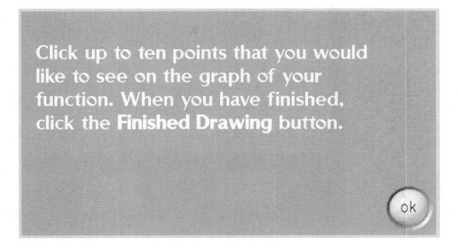

In the following screen, you have clicked ten different points.

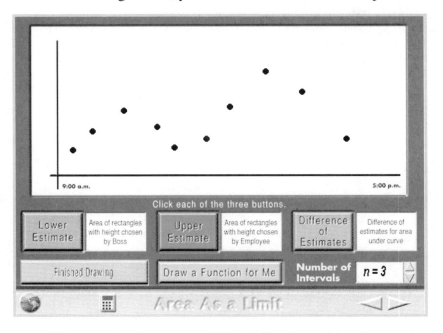

You can readily see what the curve will look like from the points you drew. When you are done, click "Finished Drawing" to see the graph of your function.

If you click "Draw a Function for Me," *Journey* will draw the graph of a function on a screen like the following:

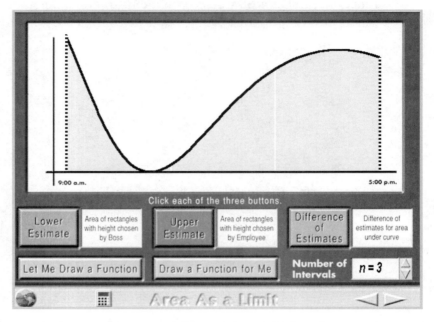

Experiment with this screen until you understand the concepts, because *Journey* is about to give you a chance to check yourself. When you are ready, click the forward arrow to move on to the following screen:

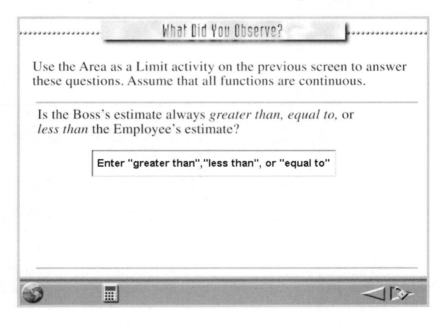

You should be able to answer this question easily—it was the basis for the dispute between the boss and the employee. When you have answered correctly, *Journey* will continue the review:

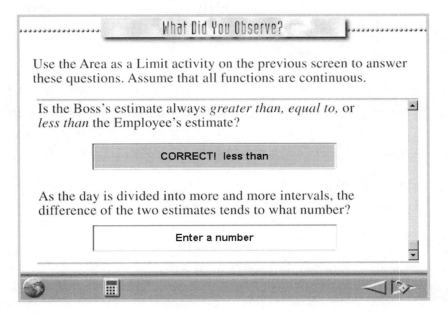

You may have to think for a moment to answer this one, but again, the answer is intuitive. When you have figured it out, and entered the correct number, *Journey* asks you one last question to review this exploration:

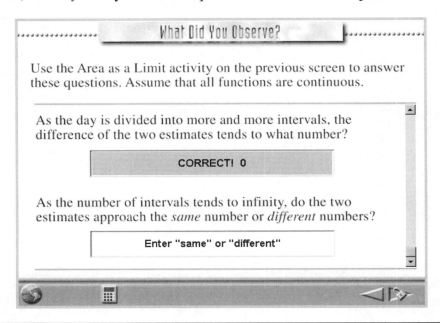

When you have answered this third question correctly, you should understand the concept behind this exploration. *Journey* states this concept in clear English:

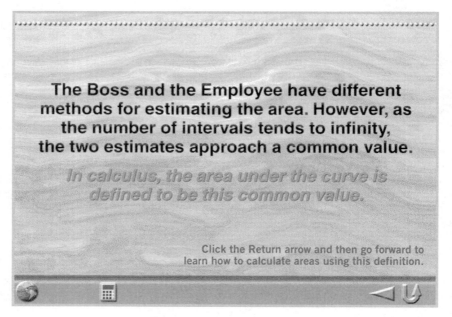

To ensure your complete understanding, *Journey* shows next an animation of two robots approaching each other and relates this animation to the concept:

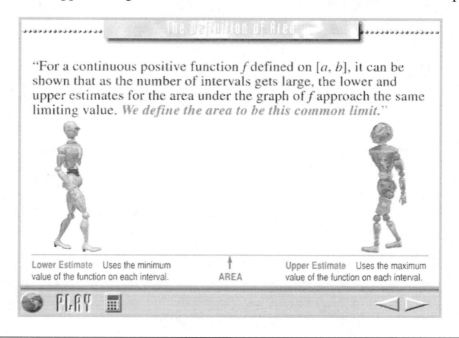

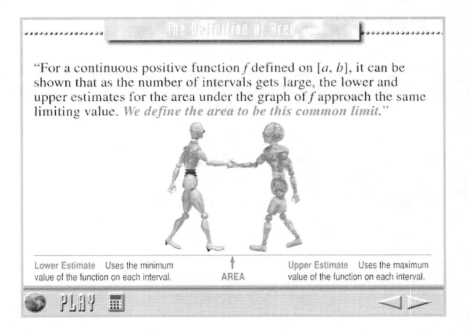

The Definition of Area

"For a continuous positive function *f* defined on [*a*, *b*], it can be shown that as the number of intervals gets large, the lower and upper estimates for the area under the graph of *f* approach the same limiting value. *We define the area to be this common limit.*"

Lower Estimate   Uses the minimum value of the function on each interval.

↑
AREA

Upper Estimate   Uses the maximum value of the function on each interval.

PLAY

Finally, in keeping with the common structure of the explorations, *Journey* gives you the mathematical formulation of this concept (click the "Listen" button to hear the narration):

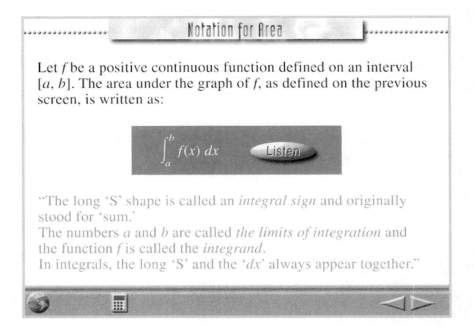

Notation for Area

Let *f* be a positive continuous function defined on an interval [*a*, *b*]. The area under the graph of *f*, as defined on the previous screen, is written as:

$$\int_a^b f(x)\, dx$$ Listen

"The long 'S' shape is called an *integral sign* and originally stood for 'sum.'
The numbers *a* and *b* are called *the limits of integration* and the function *f* is called the *integrand*.
In integrals, the long 'S' and the '*dx*' always appear together."

■ Summary of the Explorations

Now we have seen how the explorations work. Here is a complete list, by module and section, of the explorations *Journey* offers. You can use this checklist as a tool for review, making sure you have explored and mastered all the concepts presented in *Journey*.

Module 1   A Survey of Calculus and Limits

Introduction: A First Look at Limits
> The Weightlifter's Limit

Olympics (Building Models)
> Fitting the Model
> Modeling Problems

Tangents (As Limits)
> What Is a Tangent?
> Alien Invasion (Secant Approaching Tangent)
> Finding the Slope of the Secant
> Numerical Exploration (Letting *h* Approach 0)

Area (As a Limit)
> Rectangles in Circles

Finance (The Number e as a Limit)
> Start of Finance (Bank Interest)
> The Limit of $1/(1 + n)$ to the power of n
> The Paradox
> Interest Rate Problems

Module 2   Limits of Functions

Basics of Limits (Limits of Functions)
> Analysis of Meltdown (Exploring Left and Right Limits)
> The Essential Examples

The Essential Examples
> Example A (Limit of a Quotient)
> Example B (Limit of an Absolute Value)
> Example C (Limit of a Square Root)
> Example D (Limit of a Polynomial)
> Example E (Limit of a Quotient
> Example F (Limit of a sin(pi/x))

4

The Computer Algebra System

To give you the power to solve almost any calculus problem easily, *Journey* includes a Maple-supported Computer Algebra System (CAS). You can access the CAS from most of *Journey's* screens—just look for the ▦ icon on the navigation bar. Click this icon to bring up the main CAS screen:

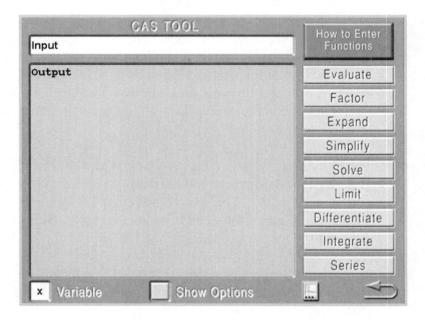

■ Entering Functions

Journey looks for functions in a certain format. It is not complicated, but it may be a bit different from the way you write them on paper. Click the "How to Enter Functions" button for a quick explanation, and you will see this screen:

How to Enter Functions

To Enter	Type In
$3x$	3*x
x^2	x^2
$x^2 - 3x + 5$	x^2-3*x+5
$\dfrac{x^3 - 5x^2}{x^4 + 1}$	(x^3-5*x^2)/(x^4+1)
$\sin x$	sin(x)
e^x	exp(x)

The purpose of *Journey's* CAS is to help you solve calculus problems quickly and to easily access mathematical functions, not to typeset formulas. Full-blown equation editors tend to be cumbersome and slow, but *Journey's* interface is straightforward and intuitive. You just have to follow a few guidelines—and the explanation, if you need a reminder, is just a mouse click away.

The first thing you will notice is that you need to specify the operator in every case. Where you would normally write $3x$, *Journey's* CAS requires you to specify $3 * x$. Spaces are ignored—$3*x$ is interpreted the same as $3 * x$—so you may use them if it makes your functions easier to read. Use the carat ($^$) for exponentiation; use the virgule ($/$) for division.

One thing you may have noticed is that you need only enter the function, not the equation. In other words, you do not need to enter the left-hand side of the equation. If you are used to writing, for example, $f(x) = 3x + 2$ or $y = 3x + 2$, in the CAS you would simply enter the function, $3 * x + 2$.

You also need to specify the variable in the function. Look at the following screen and try to spot the error:

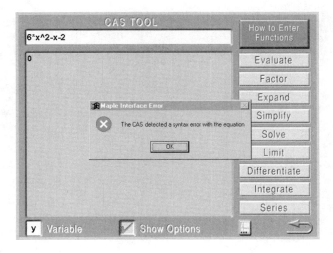

Did you find it? The function you entered, $6x^2 - x - 2$, is perfectly valid. Now look in the lower left corner of the screen to find the problem. The CAS was expecting to find a variable y in the function. Change the "Variable" box to x, and the problem goes away.

■ Using the Algebra System

You probably noticed the array of buttons on the right side of the CAS screen: "Evaluate," "Factor," "Expand," and so on. They work exactly as the button names imply, and you may already be familiar with some of these operations. Nonetheless, we will look at a couple of examples.

In the following screen, we entered the function $6x^2 - x - 2$ and clicked the "Factor" button:

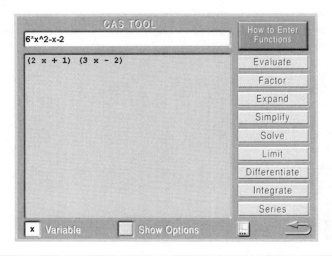

The CAS did exactly what you would expect it to do—it factored the function. If you had clicked the "Evaluate" button, it would have given you the value of the function when the variable is zero:

■ The Graphing Tool

One of the most powerful features of *Journey's* CAS is the Graphing Tool, represented by the icon on the CAS screen. Enter a function, click the Graphing Tool icon, and *Journey* will graph that function for you. For example, here is the graph of the function $6x^2 - x - 2$:

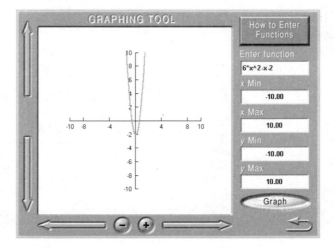

You can also enter functions directly on the Graphing Tool screen. In the following screen, we changed the function to $6x^2 - x - 4$, and then clicked the "Graph" button:

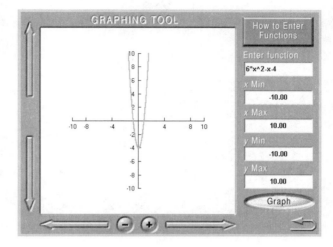

The Graphing Tool also allows you to zoom in and out in real time or pan left, right, up, or down. These are powerful features. For example, look at the following graph:

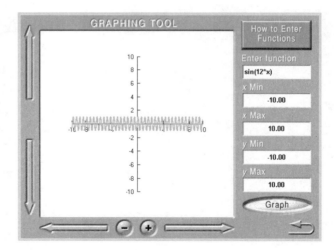

Can you tell for sure by glancing at the graph where the zero is? This is a fairly simple function, and you may remember from your Trigonometry studies that it has a zero at $x = 0$, but your functions will not always be this easy. Click the "+" button to zoom in—you can either click it repeatedly or click and hold to zoom quickly. Either method will give you a closer look:

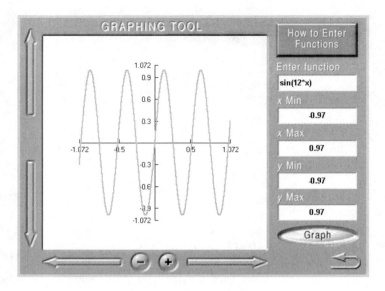

You can also zoom out using the "−" button.

The four arrows at the bottom and left of the screen also allow you to pan in any direction. In the following graph, we have panned up:

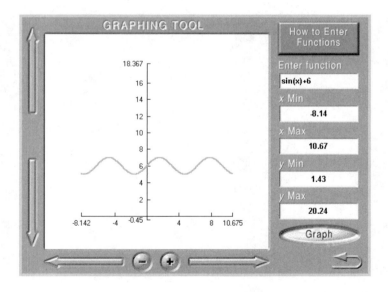

Another way of adjusting the view of the the graph is to change the x and y Min and Max. The following graph using the "normal" 10 to −10 Min and Max does not provide much useful information:

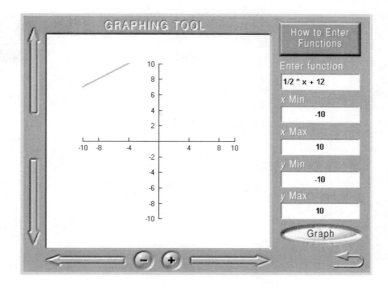

However, simply by changing the x and y Min and Max, you get a much more useful view of the same function's graph:

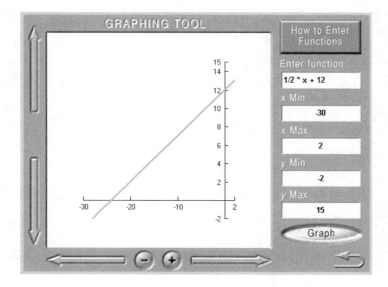

■ Options

Take a look once more at the CAS main screen:

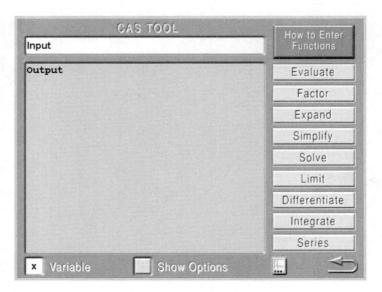

Notice the "Show Options" button at the bottom. If you click it, you can preset certain parameters. For example, in the following screen, we clicked the "Show Options" button before clicking the "Evaluate" button:

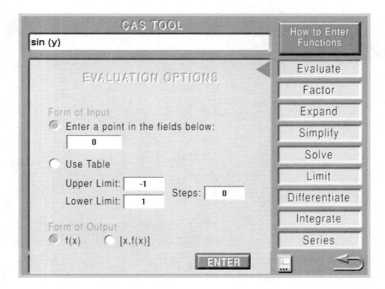

This screen allows you to tell *Journey's* CAS how you want sin *y* evaluated. For example, if you wanted to know the value of the function at *y* = 2, you would type "2" as the point and click Enter. As everyone knows, the answer is .9092974268, but it doesn't hurt to check your work.

When you are finding the limits of a function, *Journey's* CAS will give you the following options if you have the "Show Options" button checked:

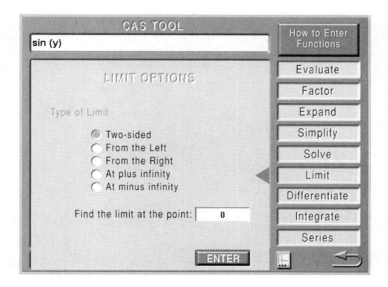

For all its ease of use, you will find *Journey's* Computer Algebra System a powerful and flexible compass to guide you on your own journey.

5 Problem Wizards and Test Wizards

■ I Don't Like Tests!

Try this: have a friend write down seven two-digit numbers. Don't peek—this is an experiment, not a test.

Now set a timer for 20 seconds. Glance at the numbers just long enough to read them—no more than 5 seconds. Immediately, start the timer and talk about something else: a class you are taking, your favorite sport, or anything but the numbers.

When the timer goes off, write down as many of the numbers as you can. Chances are you remembered most, if not all, of them.

Try it again with a new set of numbers, but set the timer to a minute. After about a minute of conversation, how many numbers could you remember? Probably not many.

Do it once more, but this time take a full minute to memorize the numbers before you start the one-minute timer. After a minute's conversation, chances are you will remember several of the numbers.

Psychologists and educators have known about this phenomenon for years. Humans have two kinds of memory: short-term and long-term. The transfer from short-term to long-term memory takes a little time—it does not happen instantaneously.

So how does Phenomenon this relate to *Journey Through Calculus*? It's simple—*Journey* gives you the opportunity to practice as long and as often as you need. The Interactive Explorations are one means you can employ to practice. The other uses *Journey's* Problem Wizard and Test Wizard.

■ The Problem Wizard: How to Get to Carnegie Hall

There is an old story—you have probably heard it—about a young person who stopped an old man on the street in New York City and asked how to get to Carnegie Hall. The old man answered, "Practice, practice, practice." That applies to calculus as well as music.

When you understand a concept, both intuitively and mathematically, you can practice applying that concept immediately through the Problem Wizard. The Problem Wizard uses special algorithms to generate a series of problems related to a specific concept. You can use the Problem Wizard as long and as often as you wish, until the concept is comfortably seated in your long-term memory.

In Chapter 2, Navigation, we briefly mentioned the Problem Wizard. You can reach it in different ways. First, take a look at the map of Module 6:

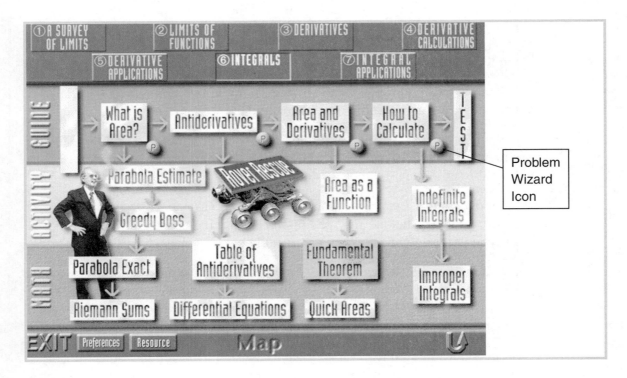

You can click the P icon any time, and *Journey* will take you to a screen such as the following:

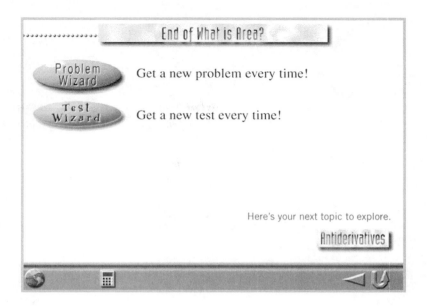

You will also arrive at this screen if you are working through a concept, through either the Guide Track, the Activity Track, or the Math Track. Yet another way is through the Resource Menu on the Map screen. You might remember this screen from Chapter 2, Navigation:

The  icon indicates problems and tests. It usually skips the introductory screen and moves directly to the Problem Wizard.

Often the Problem Wizard will give you a choice of several different types of questions. For example, in the following screen from Module 6, you can choose from four types of antiderivative problems:

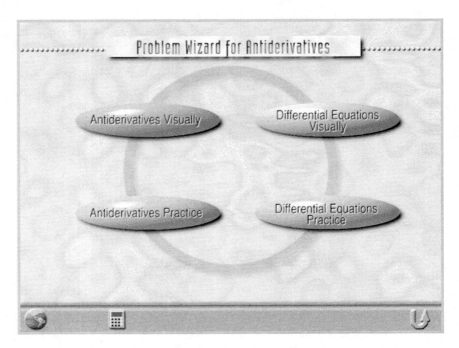

However you arrive at the Problem Wizard, it will generate problems so you can begin practicing. For example, here is a problem *Journey* generated for the end of "What is Area" section:

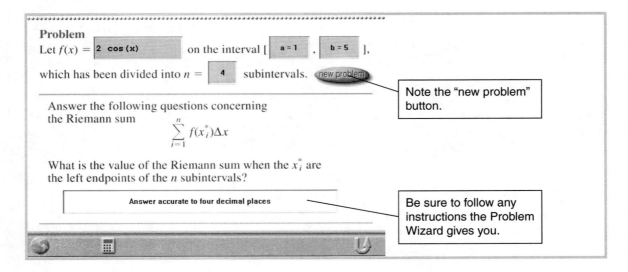

Problem

Let $f(x) = $ `2 cos(x)` on the interval [`a = 1` , `b = 5`],

which has been divided into $n = $ `4` subintervals. `new problem`

Note the "new problem" button.

Answer the following questions concerning the Riemann sum

$$\sum_{i=1}^{n} f(x_i^*)\Delta x$$

What is the value of the Riemann sum when the x_i^* are the left endpoints of the n subintervals?

Answer accurate to four decimal places

Be sure to follow any instructions the Problem Wizard gives you.

Click the mouse in the solution box at the bottom, type in your solution, and press Enter. Remember that you can use the Computer Algebra System if you need help.

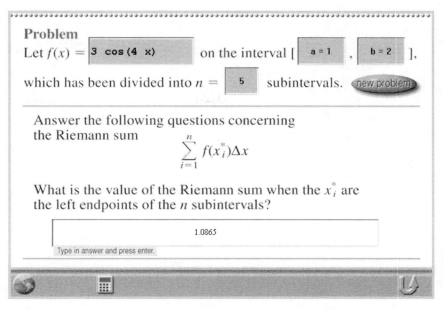

Problem

Let $f(x) = $ `3 cos (4 x)` on the interval [`a = 1` , `b = 2`],

which has been divided into $n = $ `5` subintervals. (new problem)

Answer the following questions concerning the Riemann sum

$$\sum_{i=1}^{n} f(x_i^*)\Delta x$$

What is the value of the Riemann sum when the x_i^* are the left endpoints of the n subintervals?

1.0865

Type in answer and press enter.

Journey will tell you if you have the right solution. In this case, your answer is correct, so *Journey* displays

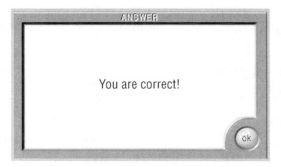

ANSWER

You are correct!

ok

If you had typed in an incorrect solution, *Journey* would have given you this feedback:

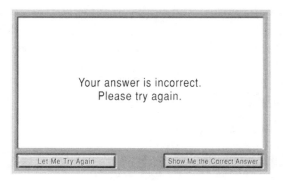

Your answer is incorrect.
Please try again.

Let Me Try Again   Show Me the Correct Answer

You can then try again or ask *Journey* to show you the correct answer.

If you wish to continue practicing, click the "new problem" button. The Problem Wizard will then generate a new problem for you, as shown:

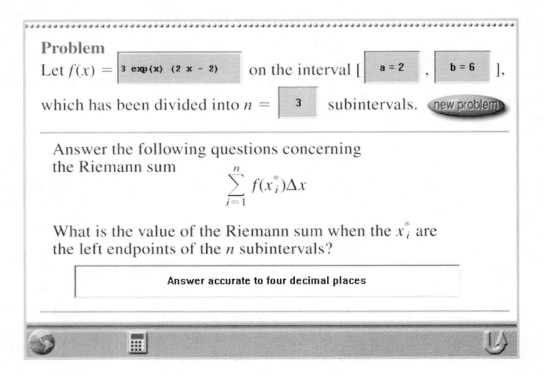

Remember that *Journey's* Computer Algebra System is available while you are working the problems.

One final note: *Journey* uses the Problem Wizard to algorithmically generate problems at the end of nearly every section. However, in a few instances, you will find a fixed set of problems or even a project. Module 5, for example, has a project for you in the Related Rates section. Module 1 is another example—some of the sections have a fixed set of problems.

■ The Test Wizard

Let's take another look at the "End of What is Area" screen:

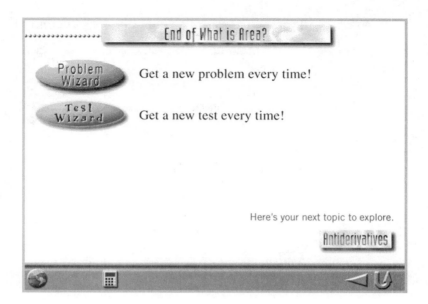

Click the 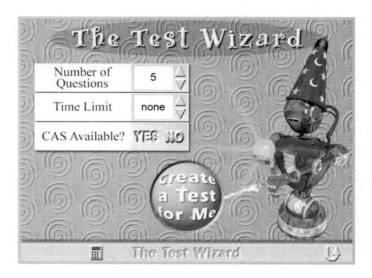 button to have *Journey's* Test Wizard create a test for you.

Journey will prompt you to tell the Test Wizard what kind of test you want:

You can adjust the number of questions, set a time limit, and decide whether you want to have the Computer Algebra System available. After you have specified your selections, click the "Create a Test for Me" button and the Test

Wizard will prepare a test for you that looks something like this:

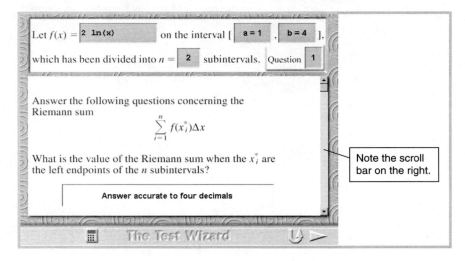

Type your answer in the same way you would in a Problem Wizard exercise. Because this is a multi-part problem, instead of pressing Enter, you use the scroll bar on the right to move to the next part of the question.

In the following screen, *Journey's* Test Wizard has noticed that you chose to use the Computer Algebra System:

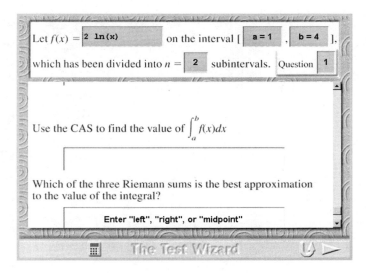

When you have answered all parts of the question, click the right arrow to move to the next question. When all the questions are answered, you will get a screen such as the following:

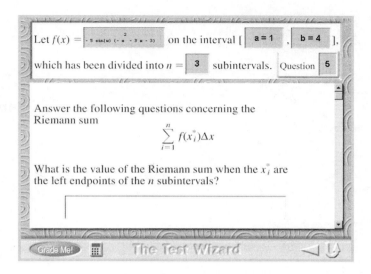

Click the "Grade Me" button, and *Journey* will grade your test and give you the appropriate feedback:

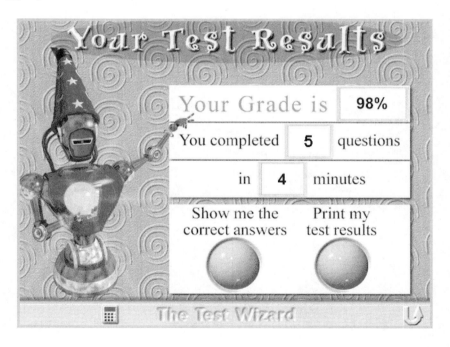

From this screen, you can ask the Test Wizard to show you the correct answers or print out your fully graded test results. If you choose to see the correct answers, you will see a screen similar to the following:

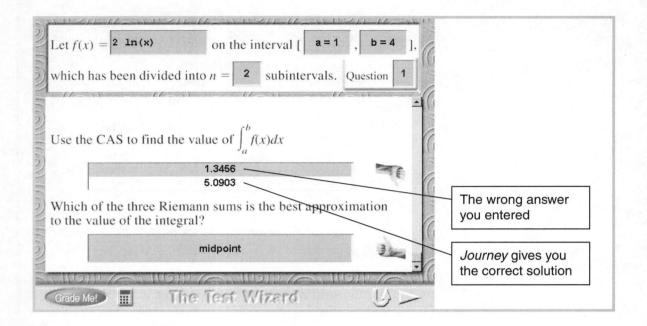

Let $f(x) =$ 2 ln(x) on the interval [a = 1 , b = 4],
which has been divided into $n =$ 2 subintervals. Question 1

Use the CAS to find the value of $\int_a^b f(x)\,dx$

1.3456

5.0903

The wrong answer you entered

Which of the three Riemann sums is the best approximation to the value of the integral?

midpoint

Journey gives you the correct solution

Grade Me!   The Test Wizard

Journey rewards you with a "thumbs up" for correct answers and gives you a "thumbs down" for the wrong solution. Unlike many critics, though, it will tell you what the correct solution is.

Using *Journey's* Test Wizard, you can create and take as many tests as you wish until you feel confident that you have mastered a particular concept.

By now you are familiar with the major sights and attractions found in this innovative and powerful calculus course, and are well prepared to get the most out of Brooks/Cole Publishing Company's *Journey Through Calculus.* Enjoy your journey!

Photo Credits

Module 1

Olympics The 400-Meter Hurdles: © Popperfoto / Archive Photos
Sebastian Coe © Popperfoto / Archive Photos
You can't catch me; I'm the gingerbread man © Popperfoto / Archive Photos
The supreme runner: what evidence now? © Popperfoto / Archive Photos
Rhind papyrus Courtesy of Avery Library, Columbia University

Module 2

House Timothy Eagan / Woodfin Camp and Associates

Module 3

Shuttle in flight © Lee F. Snyder / Photo Researchers, Inc.
Photo of earth from space Courtesy of NASA
Pioneer 10 © Frank Rossotto / The Stock Market
Mars Rover Courtesy of NASA
Mars landscape Courtesy of NASA
Computer chip Telegraph Colour Library / FPG
Yale Tablet Courtesy of Avery Library, Columbia University

Module 4

Shuttle in flight © Lee F. Snyder / Photo Researchers, Inc.
Greedy Landlord Karen Mahakian
Trump Tower Telegraph Colour Library / FPG
Oil Refinery Lester Lefkowitz / FPG
Light bulb Frank Saragnese / FPG
3-year-old twins eating ice cream cones in park Stephen Simpson / FPG
Dallas Travelpix / FPG
Alamo Square Andrew Shennan / FPG

Module 5

Alien Hitchhiking © Chip Simmons / FPG
Sandbar Shark © David Floetham / FPG
Great White Shark © David Fleetham / FPG
Greedy spaceship dealer Karen Mahakian
UFO Over Lake at Sunset © James Porto / FPG
Space Colonization © J. Baum / Science Source

Module 6

Satellite dish Stephen Simpson / FPG
Satellite dish Lester Lefkowitz / FPG
Greedy Boss series Karen Mahakian
Mars Jack Zehrt / FPG
Mars landscape Courtesy of NASA
Circuit board Telegraph Colour Library / FPG

Module 7

Spy Karen Mahakian
Step pyramid Bruce Stoddard / FPG
Pyramids VCL / FPG
Island Don Herbert / FPG
Island Don Herbert / FPG
Moscow papyrus Courtesy of Avery Library, Columbia University
Sphinx Corel Professional Photos
Power plant Fergus O'Brien / FPG
Dam Washington Alan Kearney / FPG
Elephant Haroldo de Faria Castro / FPG
Elephant Tony Ord / FPG
Flying Cds Paul & Linda Ambrose / FPG